THE
TOSA DIARY

by Ki no Tsurayuki

translated from the Japanese by
William N. Porter
BILINGUAL EDITION

TUTTLE Publishing
Tokyo | Rutland, Vermont | Singapore

ABOUT TUTTLE
"Books to Span the East and West"

Our core mission at Tuttle Publishing is to create books which bring people together one page at a time. Tuttle was founded in 1832 in the small New England town of Rutland, Vermont (USA). Our fundamental values remain as strong today as they were then—to publish best-in-class books informing the English-speaking world about the countries and peoples of Asia. The world has become a smaller place today and Asia's economic, cultural and political influence has expanded, yet the need for meaningful dialogue and information about this diverse region has never been greater. Since 1948, Tuttle has been a leader in publishing books on the cultures, arts, cuisines, languages and literatures of Asia. Our authors and photographers have won numerous awards and Tuttle has published thousands of books on subjects ranging from martial arts to paper crafts. We welcome you to explore the wealth of information available on Asia at www.tuttlepublishing.com.

Published by Tuttle Publishing, an imprint of Periplus Editions (HK) Ltd.

www.tuttlepublishing.com

© 1981 by Charles E. Tuttle Co., Inc.
Cover image: Japanese Gallery, London

All rights reserved. No part of this publication may be reproduced or utilized in any form or by any means, electronic or mechanical, including photocopying, recording, or by any information storage and retrieval system, without prior written permission from the publisher.

ISBN 978-0-8048-3695-1
ISBN 978-4-8053-0754-0 (for sale in Japan only)

First Tuttle edition published 1981

20 19 18 17   7 6 5 4 3

Printed in Singapore   1709MP

TUTTLE PUBLISHING® is a registered trademark of Tuttle Publishing, a division of Periplus Editions (HK) Ltd.

Distributed by

North America, Latin America & Europe
Tuttle Publishing
364 Innovation Drive
North Clarendon
VT 05759-9436 U.S.A.
Tel: 1 (802) 773-8930
Fax: 1 (802) 773-6993
info@tuttlepublishing.com
www.tuttlepublishing.com

Japan
Tuttle Publishing
Yaekari Building 3rd Floor
5-4-12 Osaki Shinagawa-ku
Tokyo 141 0032
Tel: (81) 3 5437-0171
Fax: (81) 3 5437-0755
sales@tuttle.co.jp
www.tuttle.co.jp

Asia Pacific
Berkeley Books Pte. Ltd.
61 Tai Seng Avenue #02-12
Singapore 534167
Tel: (65) 6280-1330
Fax: (65) 6280-6290
inquiries@periplus.com.sg
www.periplus.com

PUBLISHER'S FOREWORD

THIS early translation of a classic work of Japanese literature retains its charm more than half a century after initial publication in 1912, and it is a distinct satisfaction to present it once more for the pleasure of discerning readers. The appearance in later years of other English translations of the work has in no way diminished the value of this one, as all who appreciate writing of a truly engaging quality will recognize.

Although it has proven impossible for technical reasons to reproduce the sketch of Ki no Tsurayuki's route that appeared in the original edition, the *Tosa Diary* continues to provide the reader with a fascinating glimpse of tenth-century Japan, as well as a literary work of enduring stature. With his great experience in translating ancient Japanese poetry, William N. Porter was ideally equipped to render into English the elegant prose and many *tanka* poems in this book. The publisher takes more than the usual pleasure in offering his translation to the public.

Ki no Tsurayuki (c. 872–946), a court nobleman of high rank, was a diarist, literary theorist, and poet. He was renowned for his erudition and skill in Chinese and Japanese poetry. Between 905 and 922, he, with the assistance of others, compiled the *Kokinshu*, the first imperial anthology of poetry. His much-cited preface to that work is the first formal articulation of a Japanese poetics and established a model for future generations of poetic criticism.

William N. Porter translated many works from the Japanese between 1909 and 1914. He is best known for his challenging but artful translation of *A Hundred Verses from Old Japan: Being a Translation of the "Hyaku-nin-isshiu"* (1909), a collection of 100 specimens of Japanese classical *tanka* (poetry written in a five-line 31-syllable format in a 5-7-5-7-7 pattern) dating from the seventh to thirteenth centuries.

INTRODUCTION

THE *Tosa Nikki*, or *Tosa Diary*, was written in the year A.D. 935 by Ki no Tsurayuki, a court nobleman of high rank, who died in 946. He had been appointed Governor of the Province of Tosa, in Shikoku, in 930, the first year of the reign of the Emperor Sujaku, and the diary is an account of his journey home by sea to Kyōto, which was then the capital. The total distance is only some 200 miles, but in those days it was considered no small undertaking, and took, as the diary shows, 55 days to accomplish; this period, however, covered several long stops on the way, including a 10 days' delay at Ōminato.

The boat used to convey such an important official would, no doubt, be of more than ordinary size, but there is nothing to tell us how large she was. A cabin is mentioned; but, though we are told that on one occasion a sail was hoisted, they relied chiefly upon oars as a means of propulsion, for sails in those early days were but seldom used. They traveled very leisurely, camping each night upon shore, and remaining there the next day if the weather looked at all threatening. Mr. H. A. C. Bonar's investigations on the subject of early Japanese shipping, as given in his paper read before the Asiatic Society of Japan in 1887, supply little or no information for this early period. He mentions an old canoe which

Introduction

was dug out near Ōsaka (the ancient port of Naniwa) in the year 1878 and is now shown in the permanent exhibition of that city. Its date could not be ascertained with any certainty, but it was estimated to be over 1000 years old, which would carry it back approximately to the period of the *Tosa Diary*, and Tsurayuki's ship might very well have been something like it. Its shape is that of a large hollowed out trunk of a tree, its length is 37ft. 5 in., and greatest width 4ft. 8in.

Ki no Tsurayuki was famous as a writer both of prose and poetry. Between the years 905 and 922 he, with assistance from others, compiled the *Kokinshū*, a famous collection of early Japanese poetry, to which he contributed a preface, which is much admired for its literary though somewhat flowery style. The *Tosa Diary*, which also ranks high among the literature of Old Japan, is, however, written in a very different tone. The English reader will no doubt be struck by its artless simplicity and quiet humor, which is as welcome as it is unexpected from a Japanese nobleman of the tenth century. His sufferings from sea-sickness, his grief for the loss of his mirror, his pride when his little daughter composes a verse in reply to that made by a visitor whom he evidently dislikes, the endless verses of his own that he cannot resist quoting, and the way in which he depreciates the verses of others, as well as many other details, supply a very human touch to the diary.

A characteristic feature of his style is the contrast of

Introduction

words he introduces; such as, he 'sang a song of the East, though he was still in the Land of the West', and 'his feelings were somewhat calmed, although the sea was still very rough', &c. The late Dr. Aston in his *History of Japanese Literature* writes: 'The *Tosa Nikki* is a striking example of the importance of style. It contains no exciting adventures or romantic situations; there are in it no wise maxims or novel information; its only merit is that it describes in simple yet elegant language, and with a vein of playful humor, the ordinary life of a traveler in Japan at the time when it was written. But this has proved sufficient to give it a high rank amongst Japanese classics, and has ensured its being handed down to our own day as a most esteemed model for composition in the native Japanese style. It has been followed by many imitations, but has had no equal.'

The Japanese language as usually written is a combination of ideographic and phonetic characters, but Tsurayuki opens his diary by announcing that he intends to write it only in phonetics. As these were comparatively simple to learn, while a knowledge of the ideographs involved a profound study of the classical Chinese language, the former became known as 'the women's language' and the latter as 'the men's language'. Tsurayuki, therefore, in order to justify his use of phonetics only, writes the diary in the character of a woman and mentions himself only in the third person, which adds considerably to the difficulties of the translator.

Introduction

He also calls himself by many different names, such as *yuku hito* (the traveler), *funagimi* (the passenger), but oftenest simply *aru hito* (a certain personage). To assist the English reader, I have put in inverted commas such of these names as are supposed to indicate the writer himself.

It is not known why he decided to dispense with ideographs and to use phonetics only, which at the time had been in use for barely a hundred years; possibly it was for the sake of simplicity, and to enable the less educated to read his work. The Japanese commentators say that his rather cowardly dread of meeting the pirates and his excessive grief for his dead child would have been inconsistent with anything but a female writer. On the other hand, Tsurayuki may have emphasized these two features so as to give an artistic finish to a diary which is supposed to be written by a woman.

With regard to the numerous verses quoted, they are all, with the exception of the two 'boat songs', written in the classical *tanka* meter, which was limited to 5 lines and 31 syllables (5-7-5-7-7). The making of verses has always been one of the polite accomplishments in Japan, and Tsurayuki seldom misses an opportunity of composing. In the translation I have retained the original meter, and introduced a rhyme in the last couplet to emphasize the caesura between the third and fourth lines of the Japanese. It is a wellnigh hopeless task to attempt a translation of Japanese verses, which, while retaining the meter, is true to the original both in spirit and

Introduction

in letter, and it would not be fair to the illustrious poet to judge his work by the English version as given here. Perhaps I may paraphrase Tsurayuki as follows: 'People who read it will say to themselves that this kind of stuff is very poor. But the translator produced it with a good deal of difficulty, so they should stop whispering such cruel things about it.'

Owing to the change of calendar the dates as given in the diary are apt to lead one astray, and I have therefore given the corresponding date in the Gregorian calendar for each entry.

The accompanying sketch of the route taken by Ki no Tsurayuki is only approximately correct, for it is not possible at this date to identify with certainty all the places named in the diary. Most of those marked on the sketch were taken from an excellent map of Japan in the possession of the Hydrographic Department of the Admiralty, which I was permitted to consult, and only one or two in addition to the four unnamed stopping-places are conjectures.

I should like to record here my grateful thanks to Mr. Choichi Fujino and to Major H. Haraguchi for their kind assistance in some of the more difficult passages.

W. N. P

Oitaru wo, chichi to se-yo.

(Japanese Proverb.)

That which is old should be treated with the respect due to a father.

土佐日記

男もすなる日記といふものを、女もしてみむとてするなり。

それの年のしはすの二十日あまり一日の日の、戌の時に門出す。そのよし、いささかにものに書きつく。

ある人、縣の四年五年はて、例のことどもみなしをへて、解由などとりて住む館より出で、船に乗るべき所へわたる。かれこれ、知る知らぬ、送りす。年ごろよくくらべしつる人々なむ、わかれ難く思ひて、日しきりにとかくしつゝ、のゝしるうちに、夜更けぬ。

THE TOSA DIARY

It is generally a man who writes what is called a Diary, but now a woman will see what she can do.[1]

A. D. 935.

28 JAN. One year on the twenty-first day of the twelfth month 'a certain personage' left home at the Hour of the Dog (8.0 p.m.), which was the beginning of this modest record. He had just completed the usual period of four or five years as Governor of a Province; everything had been wound up, documents, &c., had been handed over, and now he was about to go down to the place of embarkation; for he was to travel on shipboard. All sorts of people, both friends and strangers, came to see him off, including many who had served him faithfully during the past years, and who sorrowed at the thought of losing him that day. There was endless bustle and confusion; and so with one thing and another the night drew on.

The Tosa Diary

廿二日、和泉の国までと、たひらかに願たつ。藤原のときざね船路なれど馬の餞す。上中下、酔ひあきていと怪しく、潮海のほとりにてあざれあへり。

廿三日、八木のやすのりといふ人あり。この人、国に必ずしも言ひ使ふ者にもあらざなり。これぞ、たたはしきやうにて馬の餞したる。守からにやあらむ、国人の心の常として今はとて見えざなるを心あるものは恥ぢずぞなむ来ける。これは物によりて褒むるにしもあらず。

廿四日、講師馬の餞しに出でませり。ありとある上下、童まで酔ひしれて、一文字をだに知らぬ者しが、足は十文字に踏みてぞ遊ぶ。

29 JAN. *22nd day.*—He prayed for a calm voyage to the Land of Izumi. Fujiwara no Tokisané came to 'turn his horse's head',[2] although he was to travel by sea. Upper, middle, and lower classes all drank too heavily, and, wonderful to relate, there they were on the edge of the salt sea itself all useless and incompetent![3]

30 JAN. *23rd day.*—A certain man, called Yagi no Yasunori, although he was of too high rank to have been one of his regular attendants in the Province, openly made him a farewell present. Perhaps he had not made a very good Governor; but still, the country-folk usually on an occasion like this just said good-bye, and then disappeared; and here was a kind heart which was not ashamed to come back again. This word of praise for him is not due to the present he brought!

31 JAN. *24th day.*—The Chief Priest made him a farewell present; and accordingly everybody, high and low, even the very boys, got so intoxicated, that those who did not know how to write one word found that their feet had playfully trodden the word 'ten' in the sand.[4]

The Tosa Diary

廿五日、守の館より呼びに文もて来たなり。よばれていたりて日ひと日、夜ひと夜、とかく遊ぶやうにて明けにけり。

廿六日、なほ守の館にて、あるじのヽしりて、郎等までに物かづけたり。漢詩、声あげていひけり。和歌、あるじも客人も、他人もいひあへりけり。漢詩はこれにえ書かず。和歌あるじのよめりける、

　都いで、君に逢はむとこしものをこしかひもなく別れぬるかな

となむありければ、かへる前の守のよめりける、

The Tosa Diary

1 FEB. *25th day.*—A written invitation arrived from Government House,[5] asking him to go and call. He accordingly went to call; and, what with one thing and another, all day and all night passed away pleasantly, till at last the day broke.

2 FEB. *26th day.*—Still at Government House, where the entertainment grew boisterous; the host and even the servants became uproarious. With loud voices Chinese poems were declaimed; and the host, 'the visitor' and the other guests recited Japanese verses. The Chinese poems are not recorded here;[6] but the following is the Japanese verse composed by the Governor, as host:

> From the Capital
> Far across the sea I came,
> Came to see my Lord;
> But alas! 'twas all in vain,
> For we now must part again.

Whereupon 'the former Governor' composed this in reply:

The Tosa Diary

しろたへの浪路(なみぢ)を遠(とほ)くゆきかひて我(われ)に似(に)べきはたれならなくに

他人(ことひと)びとのもありけれど、さかしきもなかるべし。とかくいひて前(さき)の守(かみ)、今(いま)のも諸共(もろとも)におりて、今(いま)のあるじも前(さき)のも手(て)取(と)り交(かは)して、酔(ゑ)ひごとに心(こころ)よげなることとして出(い)で入(い)りにけり。

廿七日、大津(おほつ)より浦戸(うらど)をさして漕(こ)ぎ出(い)づ。かくあるうちに京(きゃう)にて生(う)まれたりし女子(をむなご)、国(くに)にては俄(にはか)に失(う)せにしかば、この頃(ごろ)の出立(いでたち)いそぎを見(み)れど、何事(なにごと)もいはず。京(きゃう)へ帰(かへ)るに女子(をむなご)のなきのみぞ悲(かな)しび恋(こ)ふる。ある人々(ひとびと)もえ耐(た)へず。この間(あひだ)に、ある人(ひと)の書(か)きて出(い)だせる歌(うた)、

> I, too, traveled far
> O'er the stormy road of waves
> White with crested foam;
> Scare, I think, another man
> Would have faced the risks we ran!

There were also verses composed by many others, but they were quite worthless. Having recited these, the late and the present Governors descended together; the present and the late hosts went forth hand in hand, in good fellowship and the best of spirits.

3 FEB. *27th day.*—They started from Ōtsu and began to row to Urato. His little daughter,[7] who had been born in the Capital, had died a short time previously in the Province very suddenly; and now, when, as we see, he was departing in haste, what was he to say! All his love was changed to grief, for he will now have no little daughter to return with him to the Capital. It was more than most men could bear; but in this case 'a certain personage' dragged out the following verse:

都へとおもふをもの、かなしきはかへらぬ人のあればなりけり

また、ある時には、

あるものと忘れつゝなほなき人をいづらと問ふぞ悲しかりける

といひける間に、鹿児崎といふ所に、守のはらから、また他人、これかれ酒なにと持て追ひきて、磯におり居て別れ難きことを言ふ。守の館の人々の中にこの来たる人々ぞ、心あるやうには言はれほのめく。かく別れ難くいひて、かの人々の口網ももろ持ちにて、この海辺にて担ひいだせる歌、

The Tosa Diary

> Though I now return
> To my home, the Capital,
> Sad it is to think
> One for whom I mourn in vain
> Never will return again.

He composed the following also upon the same occasion:

> Could I e'er forget
> What is past, I still should grieve
> If she were not here;
> Seeking for her, I should say,
> 'Where's my little girl today?'

Such were his words. At a place named Cape Kago the Governor's brother,[8] some strangers and many others hurried down to the shore with *saké* and other good things to bid a sad farewell; and all the people from Government House, who had come here, spoke softly in the kindness of their hearts. To express their grief at parting, these good people clustered together upon the sea-shore and dragged out the following verse,—which was as heavy as a net full of fishes!

The Tosa Diary

をしと思ふ人やとまるとあしがものうちむれてこそわれはきにけれ

といひてありければ、いといたく愛で、ゆく人のよめりける、

棹させど底ひもしらぬわたつみのふかきこゝろを君に見るかな

といふ間に楫取ものゝ、哀も知らで、おのれし酒をくらひつれば、早く往なむとて「潮満ちぬ。風も吹きぬべし」とさわげば、船に乗りなむとす。この折にある人々、折節につけて、漢詩ども時に似つかはしき言ふ。また、ある人、西国なれど甲斐歌など言ふ。かくうたふに、「ふなやかたの塵も散り、空ゆく雲もたゞよひぬ。」とぞ言ふなる。

今宵浦戸に泊る。藤原のときざね、橘のすゑひら、他人々追ひきたり。

Like a flock of ducks[9]
Here among the reeds are we;
Deeply we regret
Thy departure, and we would
Keep thee with us, if we could.

On this 'the traveler' with the greatest appreciation replied:

Sounding with my pole
Bottom is there none; and thus
Like the Sea-God's realm,
Bottomless my loving heart,
When I think we now must part.

The steersman,[10] who had himself been freely eating and drinking *saké* while all this was going on, now remorselessly said they must get away at once; for the tide was full, and he feared the wind might blow and they would have a rough tossing in the ship. Just about this time several others wrote appropriate verses; they were Chinese poems and I have no doubt they were worthy of the occasion; 'a certain personage' also sang a song of the East,[11]—though he was still in the Land of the West. While these verses were being sung, we are told, even the dust in the cabin began to blow about and the clouds to

廿八日、浦戸より漕ぎ出でて、大湊を追ふ。この間にはやくの守の子、山口ちみね、酒よきものども持てきて船に入れたり。ゆくゆく飲み食ふ。

廿九日、大湊に泊れり。くす師、振りはへて屠蘇、白散、酒加へて持て来たり。志あるに似たり。

元日、なほ同じ泊なり。白散をあるもの夜の間とて、ふなやかたにさしはさめりければ、風に吹きならさせて海に入れて、え飲まずなりぬ。芋じ、あらめも歯固めもなし。かうやうの物なき国なり。求めしもおかず。たゞ押鮎の口をのみぞ吸ふ。この吸

scud across the sky! That evening a stop was made at Urato, to which spot Fujiwara no Tokisané and Tachibana no Suehira followed.[12]

4 FEB. *28th day.*—They set out rowing from Urato and made for Ōminato, where Yamaguchi no Chiminé, the son of a former Governor, came with *saké* and good things to eat, which he put aboard the boat. There will be plenty to eat and drink during the voyage!

5 FEB. *29th day.*—They remained at Ōminato, and the Doctor paid a visit, in order to present some spiced *saké* and *byakusan* appropriate to the season, as well as ordinary *saké*;[13] this he did from pure kindness of heart.

6 FEB. *New Year's Day.*—Still they remained at the same place. The *byakusan* had been placed for safe-keeping during the night in the ship's cabin; but the wind which is usual at this time of year got up and blew it all into the sea. They had nothing left to drink; no potatoes, no seaweed and no rice-cakes; the neighbourhood could supply nothing of this kind, and so their wants could not be satisfied. They could do nothing more

The Tosa Diary

ふ人々の口を押鮎もし思ふやうあらむや。「けふは都のみぞ思ひやらる、こへの門のしりくべ縄のなよしのかしら、柊木らいかにぞ」とぞいひあへなる。

二日、なほ大湊に泊れり。講師、物、酒おこせたり。

三日、同じ所なり。もし風浪のしばしと惜む心やあらむ、心もとなし。

四日、風吹けば、え出でたゝず。まさつら、酒よき物奉れり。このかうやうに物持て来る人に、なほしもえあらで、いさゝけわざせさす。物もなし。にぎはゝしきやうなれど、負くる心地す。

than suck the head of a trout. What must the trout have thought of everybody sucking it in turn! That day he could think of nothing but the Capital, and talk of nothing but the straw rope stretched across the Gates of the Imperial Palace, the mullet heads and the holly.[14]

7 FEB. *2nd day.*—Still at Ōminato. The Chief Priest sent a gift of food and *saké*.

8 FEB. *3rd day.*—In the same place. I wonder if the wind and waves had a tender feeling for him, as they seemed to wish to delay him for some time? He certainly had no tender feeling for them!

9 FEB. *4th day.*—No start was made, as a high wind was still blowing. Masatsura presented a gift of *saké* and other good things. A man who came with presents like this ought not to have come in vain; but there was literally nothing to offer him; and, though it all looked lively enough, his spirits were very low.

The Tosa Diary

五日、風浪止まねば、なほ同じ所にあり。人々絶えずとぶらひに来。

六日、きのふのごとし。

七日になりぬ。同じ湊にあり。けふは白馬を思へど、かひなし。たゞ浪の白きのみぞ見ゆる。かゝる間に人の家の池と名ある所より、鯉はなくて鮒よりはじめて川のも、海のも、こともども、長櫃に担ひつゞけておこせたり。若菜ぞけふをば知らせたる。歌あり。その歌、

浅茅生の野辺にしあれば水もなき池につみつるわかななりけり

10 FEB. *5th day.*—As the wind and waves had not gone down, they still remained at the same spot, and many people constantly came to call upon him.

11 FEB. *6th day,* is the same as yesterday.

12 FEB. The *7th day* came and found them still at the same port. This day his thoughts were fixed upon the Festival of the Grey Horse;[15] but it was of no good wishing for that, for all he could see were the white waves. About this time a present arrived from somebody's estate which was called Iké;[16] a long box slung from a pole containing, not carp, but many other kinds of river and sea fish, beginning with goldfish; also green vegetables packed in a basket, pheasants, game, and flowers. The green vegetables[17] reminded him what day it was, for they bore the following verse:

> Water is there none
> On the wild and lonely moor
> Where the rushes grow;
> But from Iké, see, we bring
> Fresh green shoots of early spring.

いとをかし。この池といふは、所の名なり。よき人の男につきて下りて住みけるなり。この長櫃の物は、みな人、童までにくれたれば、飽き満ちて船子どもは腹鼓をうちて、海をさへおどろかして浪たてつべし。かくて、この間に事おほかり。けふ、破籠持たせてきたる人、その名などぞや、いま思ひ出でむ。この人、歌よまむと思ふ心ありてなりけり。とかくいひて、浪の立つなること、憂へいひてよめる歌、

ゆくさきにたつ白浪の声よりもおくれて泣かむわれやまさらむ

とぞよめる。いと大声なるべし。持てきたる物よりは歌はいかゞあらむ。この歌をこれかれあはれがれども、ひとりも返しせず。しつべき人も交れゝど、これをのみいたがり、物を飲み食ひて夜更けぬ。この歌ぬし、「またまからず」といひて立ちぬ。ある人の子の童なる、密に言ふ。「まろ、この歌の返しせむ」と言ふ。驚きて「いとをかし

A very amusing verse. This estate called Iké, he was told, was occupied by a lady of rank, who had come down from the Capital and who lived there with her husband. The contents of the long box were distributed among all, even the boys were not forgotten; they all had abundance to eat, and the sailors patted their bellies contentedly. The sea was so shocked at the sight, that the waves began to get up, and while this was going on many things happened. This day a man arrived with a servant carrying a box of food; what *was* his name? Perhaps I shall think of it soon. Well, this man had it in his mind that he would compose a poem. He talked about it a good deal, and then, taking as his subject the sad sight of the waves getting up, composed this:

On thy journey hence,
Though the billows white with spray
Ever louder roar,
When to thee 'Farewell' I call,
My cries shall surpass them all.

Well, that was his verse. He must surely have had a very loud voice, and his poem was hardly as good as what he brought. Every one sympathized with this verse, but nobody composed one in reply; and, though there were many there who could have done so, they merely

きとかな。よみてむやは、よみつべくは、はやいへかし」と言ふ。「まからず、とて立ちぬる人を待ちてよまむ」とて求めけるを、夜更けぬとにやありけむ、やがて往にけり。「そもそもいかゞよんだる」と、いぶかしがりて問ふ。この童さすがに恥ぢていはず。強ひて問へばいへる歌、

ゆく人も泊るも袖のなみだ川みぎはのみこそぬれまさりけれ

となむよめる。かくはいふものか。うつくしければにやあらむ、いと思はずなり。「童ごとにては何かはせむ。女翁ておしつべし。悪しくもあれ、いかにもあれ、たよりあらば遣らむ」とておかれぬめり。

bore it in silence. And so with eating and drinking the night drew on, till the poet got up and went off, promising to come back again. 'A certain personage's' little child[18] whispered, 'I will make a verse in reply to his.' What a surprise! and how very amusing! You can't compose a verse! If you think you can, please let us have it at once. She waited a moment for the man who had gone out and had promised to return, and then went to look for him; but the night had grown late, and he did not come back. Meanwhile we asked ourselves doubtfully, what kind of verse this would be. The child was shy and unwilling to give it, but when spoken to firmly she repeated this:

> See, the shore is wet
> With the stream of tears which pours
> From the sleeves of those
> Who upon the beach must stay,
> Or who go upon their way.

That was her verse. How clever of her to get an idea like that! I did not think she could have done it. How could a mere child do so well? It is worthy of a woman or an old man. Well, whether it is poor, or whatever it is, it shall be carefully preserved, in case there may be an opportunity to send it to the poet.

八日、さはる事ありて、なほ同じ所なり。今宵、月は海にぞ入る。これを見て、業平君の「やまのはにげて入れずもあらなむ」といふ歌なむおもほゆる。もし海辺にてよま、しかば「浪立ちさへて入れずもあらなむ」ともよみてましや。いまこの歌を思ひ出で、ある人のよめりける、

　　　てる月のながる、見ればあまの川いづるみなとは海にざりける

とや。

13 FEB. *8th day.*—Something or other was wrong, and they still remained where they were. That evening the moon sank into the sea. The poet Narihira once watched the setting moon and sang:

'Would the hills but fly away
Longer might the moonlight stay.'[19]

If the poet, when he composed this, had been on the sea-shore, he would no doubt have written:

Would the waves but bar the way
Longer might the moonlight stay.

Meditating still upon the verse, 'a certain personage' composed this:

Forward sails the moon
On the River of the Sky[20]
Shining overhead;
Like the lovely moon may we
Leave this port and put to sea.

There!

The Tosa Diary

九日、つとめて大湊より奈半の泊を追はむとて、漕ぎ出でけり。これかれ互に、国の境の内はとて、見送りに来る人あまたが中に、藤原のときざね、橘のすえひら、長谷部のゆきまさ等なむ、御館より出で給びし日よりこゝかしこに追ひくる。この人々ぞ志ある人なりける。この人々の深き志は、この海にも劣らざるべし。これよりいまは漕ぎ離れてゆく。これを見送らむとてぞ、この人どもは追ひきける。かくて漕ぎゆくまにまに海の辺にとまれる人も遠くなりぬ。船の人も見えずなりぬ。岸にもいふ事あるべし。船にも思ふことあれど、かひなし。かゝれど、この歌を独言にして止みぬ。

おもひやる心は海を渡れどもふみしなければ知らずやあるらむ

14 FEB. *9th day.*—They set out from Ōminato the first thing in the morning and rowed on, intending to stop at Nawa. All united in coming to bid him farewell (now that they were passing the boundaries of the Province); among many others, Fujiwara no Tokisané, Tachibana no Suehira, and Hasabé no Yukimasa, &c. From the day he left his Official Residence, people all the way along the route had come to see him off, and they all did it from kindness of heart; in fact, their kind hearts seemed to be as bottomless as the sea. At this spot, then, they parted and rowed on, for it was here that these people had come to see him off. After this, as they rowed gently forward, those who remained upon the sea-shore grew further and further away, and they in their turn could no longer see those in the boat; from the shore they could not speak to the ship, and, if the ship called to them, it was all in vain. This being so, he could only recite the following verse to himself:

> Far across the sea
> In my heart I fly to you
> Bidding you farewell;
> But no written word, alas!
> From the ship to you may pass.

かくて宇多の松原をゆき過ぐ。その松の数幾そばく、幾千歳へたりと知らず。もとごとに浪うちよせ枝ごとに鶴ぞ飛びかよふ。おもしろしと見るに耐へずして船人のよめる歌、

　見渡せば松のうれごとにすむ鶴は千代のどちとぞ思ふべらなる

とや。この歌は所を見るに、えまさらず。かくあるを見つ、漕ぎゆくまにまに、山も海もみな暮れ、夜更けて西ひむがしも見えずして、天気のこと楫取の心にまかせつ。男もならはぬは、いとも心細し。まして、女は船底に頭をつきあて、音をのみぞ泣く。かく思へば、船子楫取は船唄うたひて、何とも思へらず。そのうたふ歌は、

After this they passed the pine forest of Uta. I know not how many pine trees there were there, nor for how many thousand years they had lived.[21] The ripples lapped against the foot of each, and amid the branches of each the storks flitted about. Overcome by such a charming prospect 'the seafarer' composed this:

> On the shore the storks
> Perched amid the pine tree tops
> Charm my roving gaze;
> For a thousand years, I ween,
> Storks and pines fast friends have been.

There! And the song is no more lovely than was the prospect. Still admiring the beautiful scene, they rowed gently forward; mountains and sea all became dim, and the night drew on. As he could no longer distinguish east from west, he left all thought about the weather to the steersman. Those of the men who were unused to the sea began to feel gloomy and pensive, while the women laid their heads upon the bottom of the boat and cried aloud. But the steersman and sailors thought nothing of it all and sang their boat song; this is it:

The Tosa Diary

春の野にてぞ音をば泣く。わか薄に、手きるきるつんだる菜を、親やまぼるらむ、姑や食ふらむ。かへらや。夜んべのうなゐもがな。銭乞はむ。そらごとをして、おぎのりわざをして、銭も持て来ず、おのれだにこず。

これならず多かれども書かず。これらを人の笑ふを聞きて、海は荒るれども心は少しなぎぬ。かく行きくらして泊にいたりて、翁人ひとり、たう女ひとり、あるがなかに、心地あしみして、物もものし給はでひそまりぬ。

十日、けふはこの奈半の泊にとまりぬ。

In the fields this fine spring day
I have cut my hand
With the long grass growing there,
And I cry aloud
As I pick the greens;
Endless is my parent's greed,
But my mother must I feed.
And, when I go home,
Those I picked last night,—
They were pilfered by a thief,
One who took the greens on tick
Leaving not a cent, alack!
And he has not yet come back.[22]

There was a good deal more of this sort of thing, but I will not record it. On hearing the others laughing at it, his feelings were somewhat calmed, although the sea was still very rough. It was now quite dark as they rowed forward, and on getting to their stopping-place 'a solitary old man' and a solitary old woman among all the others, feeling unwell, took no food and retired to rest.[23]

15 FEB. *10th day.*—Today they remained at this stopping-place, Nawa.

The Tosa Diary

十一日、暁に船を出だして室津を追ふ。人みなまだ寝たれば海のありやうも見えず。ただ月を見てぞ、西ひむがしをば知りける。かかる間にみな夜明けて、手あらひ、例の事どもして昼になりぬ。いまし、羽根といふ所にきぬ。わかき童、この所の名を聞きて「羽根といふ所は鳥の羽のやうにやある」と言ふ。まだ幼き童の言なれば、人々笑ふ時にありける女童なむ、この歌をよめる、

まことにて名に聞く所羽根ならば飛ぶがごとくにみやこへもがな

とぞいへる。男も女もいかでとく都へもがなと思ふ心あれば、この歌よしとにはあらねど、げにと思ひて人々わすれず。この羽根といふ所問ふ童のついでにぞ、また昔へ人思ひ出で、いづれの時にか忘る、。けふはまして母の悲しがる、事は、くだりし

16 FEB. *11th day.*—The boat started at break of day and headed for Murotsu. They were all still half asleep, and accordingly took no notice of the condition of the sea. But the position of the moon indicated which was east and which was west, and so the day gradually became light. They washed their hands, performed their toilets, and by that time it was noon. At last they arrived at a place called Hané.[24] A little child, on hearing the name of the place, asked if Hané got its name from the wings of a bird; and, while they were all laughing at such a childish question, a little girl composed this verse:

If this place Hané
Chance to have a pair of wings,
As its name implies,
May they help us in our need
To the Capital with speed.

So she spoke. And, though it may not be a very good verse, everybody, men and women alike, who really wished in their hearts for a speedy voyage to the Capital, pondered it over and kept it in mind. This child's question about the spot called Hané again reminded him of one who was gone. When will she ever be forgotten! Her mother, too, grieved today more than ever, and quoted an old verse to the effect that

The Tosa Diary

時の人の数足らねば、古歌に「数は足らでぞ帰るべらなる」と言ふことを思ひ出で、人のよめる、

世の中に思ひやれども子を恋ふる思ひにまさる思ひなきかな

といひつゝなむ。

十二日、雨降らず。ふむとき、これもちが船の遅れたりし。奈良志津より室津にきぬ。

十三日の暁に、いさゝかに雨ふる。しばしありて止みぬ。女これかれ、ゆあみなどせむとて、あたりのよろしき所におりてゆく。海を見やれば、

there is one missing out of those who went down from the Capital:

'Was there in the flock last year
One who does not reappear?'[25]

Thinking over these words, 'somebody' composed this:

In the midst of life
Cares in plenty though there be,
Yet the little child
Whom I loved beyond compare
Was by far my greatest care.[26]

And thus he expressed his feelings.

17 FEB. *12th day.*—The rain stopped, and the boat containing Fumitoki and Koremochi, who had been left behind, arrived at Murotsu from Narashitsu.

18 FEB. *13th day.*—The rain was gently falling at daybreak, but it soon stopped, and then men and women together went down to a suitable place in the

The Tosa Diary

雲もみな浪とぞ見ゆる海士もがないづれか海と問ひて知るべく

となむ歌よめる。さて、十日あまりなれば月おもしろし。船に乗り始めし日より船には紅こくよき衣きず。それは「海の神に怖ぢて」といひて、何の蘆蔭にことづけて、ほやのつまのいずし、すしあはびをぞ、心にもあらぬはぎにあげて見せける。

十四日、暁より雨降れば同じ所に泊れり。船君節忌す。精進物なければ、午刻より後に、楫取の昨日釣りたりし鯛に、銭なければ、米をとりかけておちられぬ。かゝる事なほありぬ。楫取、また鯛持てきたり。米、酒、しばしばくる。楫取、気色あしからず。

vicinity and had a hot bath.[27] Looking out over the sea, he composed this verse:

> Overhead the clouds
> Look to me like rippling waves;
> Were the fishers here,
> 'Which is sea, and which is sky?'
> I would ask, and they'd reply.

Well, as it was after the tenth day, the moon was particularly beautiful. All these days, since first he set foot aboard ship, he had never worn his handsome bright scarlet costume, because he feared to offend the God of the Sea;[28] yet ...

19 FEB. *14th day.*—Rain was falling at daybreak, so they remained where they were. 'The passenger' was fasting, and, though it was now past the Hour of the Horse (noon), he had not even taken any vegetable food. But the steersman on the previous day had caught a bream; so having no coppers he successfully negotiated some rice for it. This transaction was often repeated, and he frequently traded rice and *saké*, whenever the steersman happened to catch bream; and the latter's countenance became quite jovial in consequence.

十五日、けふ、小豆粥煮ず。口をしく、なほ日のあしければ、ゐざるほどにぞ、けふ、廿日あまり経ぬる。徒に日を経れば、人々海をながめつゝぞある。女の童のいへる、

　立てばたつるればまたゐる吹く風と浪とは思ふどちにやあるらむ

いふかひなき者、いへるには、いと似つかはし。

十六日、風浪止まねば、なほ同じ所に泊れり。たゞ海に浪なくして、いつしか御崎といふ所渡らむとのみなむ思ふ。風浪とにに止むべくもあらず。ある人のこの浪立つを見てよめる歌、

20 FEB. *15th day.*—This day no rice and bean gruel was cooked, and, as it was an unlucky day, they crawled slowly along, much to his regret.[29] Today the voyage had already lasted more than twenty days, and they were but as so many days wasted. While all were gazing out to sea, a little girl recited this:

> When the breezes drop
> Quickly do the waves subside,
> When the wind gets up
> Then the waves again arise;
> Comrade-like they sympathize.

This is, no doubt, hardly worth giving, but it is very appropriate.

21 FEB. *16th day.*—As the wind and waves had not gone down, they remained where they were. He could think of nothing but, 'When will these wind-blown waves subside, so that we may weather this terrible headland?' However, as the wind and waves would not cease, 'a certain personage' took these breaking waves as a subject, and composed this verse:

霜だにもおかぬかたぞといふなれど浪の中には雪ぞ降りける

さて、船に乗りし日よりけふまでに廿日あまり五日になりにけり。

十七日、曇れる雲なくなりて曉月夜いとおもしろければ、船を出だして漕ぎゆく。この間に、雲のうへも海の底も同じごとくになむありける。むべも昔の男は「棹は穿つ浪の上の月を。船は襲ふ海の内の空を」とはいひけむ。聞きされに聞けるなり。また、ある人のよめる歌、

みなそこの月のうへより漕ぐ船の棹にさはるは桂なるらし

> Never hoar-frost falls
> On the ocean stretching wide,
> As is truly said;
> Yet the wave-crests seem to be
> Tipped with snow far out at sea.

Ah well! that day they had been traveling five-and-twenty days on shipboard.[30]

22 FEB. *17th day.*—The heavy clouds cleared away, and the moonlight just before daybreak was very beautiful. The boat set out, and they went on rowing. What could the clouds overhead and the sea beneath be compared to? He rather fancied that when the moon is reflected in the waves and (the sailor) plunges his pole down, the poets of old would have said that the vessel was attacking the heavens themselves in mid-ocean. He thought he had heard something of the kind, but was not sure. 'A certain personage' then composed this:

> As I row along,
> At the bottom of the sea
> Lies the lovely moon;
> There's a bush that grows on it,[31]
> Is it that my pole has hit?

The Tosa Diary

これを聞きてある人のまたよめる、

かげ見れば浪の底なるひさかたの空漕ぎ渡るわれぞわびしき

かくいふ間に、夜やうやく明けゆくに、楫取等「黒き雲にはかに出できぬ。風吹きぬべし。御船返してむ」といひて船かへる。この間に雨ふりぬ。いとわびし。

十八日、なほ同じ所にあり。海あらければ船いださず。この泊、遠く見れども、近く見れどもいとおもしろし。かゝれども苦しければ何事もおもほえず。男どちは、心やりにやあらむ、漢詩など言ふべし。船も出ださで徒らなれば、ある人のよめる、

Somebody on hearing this replied:[32]

When I see its light
'Neath the waves, I seem to be
Rowing all alone
Far across the heavenly sky,—
Lone and desolate am I.

With these words day at last broke, and the ship's officers[33] said, 'Black clouds have unexpectedly come up, a storm is approaching and the gallant ship must put back again.' So they returned; just then the rain began to fall and he felt very melancholy.

23 FEB. *18th day.*—They were still at the same spot. As long as the sea remains rough they will never get there. This stopping-place was very beautiful, whether looked at from afar or close at hand; but under the present conditions they were all too weary to take any pleasure in it. In order to pass the time, as it was hopeless to expect the boat to start, the men composed classical verses, &c., together, and 'a certain personage' produced this:

The Tosa Diary

いそふりの寄する磯には年月をいつとも分かぬ雪のみぞふる

この歌は常にせぬ人のことなり。また人のよめる、

風による浪の磯にはうぐひすも春もえしらぬ花のみぞ咲く

この歌どもを少しよろしと聞きて、船の長しける翁、月日頃の苦しき心やりによめる、

立つ浪を雪か花かと吹く風ぞ寄せつ、人をはかるべらなる

On this sandy shore
Never cease the waves to break
Year and month alike;
Though 'tis white as if with snow,
When it fell I do not know.

This verse was like an amateur's attempt, so he tried again as follows:

Though upon the shore
Wind-blown waves break into foam
White like flowers in bloom,
Neither nightingales nor spring
Knew these flowers were blossoming.

On hearing it said that these verses were pretty good, 'the venerable master of the ship,'[34] to distract his thoughts, which had been gloomy for a month, composed this:

Driven by the wind,
Stormy billows getting up
Crested white with foam
Make me think them tipped with snow,
Or that 'tis the flowers that blow.

The Tosa Diary

この歌どもを人の何かといふを、ある人聞きふけりてよめり。その歌よめる文字三十文字あまり七文字、人みな、えあらで笑ふやうなり。歌ぬし、いと気色悪しくてゑず。学べども、え学ばず。書けりとも、え読みすゑがたかるべし。けふだにいひ難し。まして後にはいかならむ。

十九日、日あしければ船出ださず。

二十日、昨日のやうなれば船出ださず。みな人々憂へ嘆く。苦しく心もとなければ、ただ日の経ぬる数を、けふいくか、二十日、三十日と数ふれば、およびもそこなはれぬべし。いとわびし。夜はいも寝ず。二十日の夜の月出でにけり。山のはもなくて海の中よりぞ出でくる。かうやうなるを見てや、むかし安倍仲麻呂といひける人は、唐

Several people criticized these verses, and one man, who was much interested in them, made another one. But, as his verse had seven-and thirty syllables,[35] the others could not help laughing. The poet, however, kept a grave face and did not even smile. I could not make a verse like that if I tried; if it was written down, I doubt if I could read it; and if I find it hard now, who could ever manage it in the future?

24 FEB. *19th day.*—The weather was bad, so the boat could not start.

25 FEB. *20th day.*—Just as yesterday the boat could not start. All the people were sighing most dolefully, for their hearts were sad at wasting so many days. How many did they amount to already? Twenty? Thirty? It would make my fingers ache to count them. At night he could not sleep and was in a melancholy mood. The rising moon, twenty days old, came up out of the midst of the sea, for there were no mountain-tops (for it to rise from). With reference to that, men say that in the old days, when Abe no Naka Maro[36] was about to cross over from China on his return, some of the country-folk at the place of his embarkation gave him a farewell ban-

The Tosa Diary

に渡りて帰り来ける時に、船に乗るべき所にて、かの国人馬の餞し、わかれ惜しみて、かしこの漢詩作りなどしける。あかずやありけむ、二十日の夜の月出づるまでぞありける。その月は海よりぞ出でける。これを見てぞ仲麻呂のぬし「我が国にかゝる歌をなむ神代より神もよんたび、今は上中下の人も、かうやうに別れ惜しみ、よろこびもあり、かなしびもある時にはよむ」とてよめりける歌、

あをうなばらふりさけ見れば春日なる三笠の山にいでし月かも

とぞよめりける。かの国人聞き知るまじくおもほえたれども、ことの心を男文字に、さまを書き出だして、この詞伝へたる人にいひ知らせければ、心をや聞き得たりけむ、いと思ひの外になむ愛でける。唐とこの国とは言異なるものなれど、月の影は同じことなるべければ、人の心も同じことにやあらむ。さていま、そのかみを思ひやりてある人のよめる歌、

The Tosa Diary

quet, to show their regret at his departure, and he then composed a classical poem. They did not grow weary until the moon rose on the night of the twentieth day; and it was from the sea that the moon rose then also. While gazing at it the great master Naka Maro (said), 'In my land in the time of the Gods the Deities themselves always composed poems like this; and still today all the people of the upper, middle and lower classes do the same, when bidding a sad farewell, and in times of joy and sorrow.' He then composed this:

> 'I, while gazing far
> O'er the blue sea stretching wide,
> Seem to see the moon
> Rising o'er Mount Mikasa
> At the Shrine of Kasuga.'[37]

That is the verse. Though the people of that land did not seem to understand it when they heard it, yet when the proper words were written down in men's characters (Chinese ideographs) they understood it perfectly, and were much pleased with it.[38] In that far away land of China the language was different, but the moonlight was still the same, and would not the hearts of men be the same also? With his thoughts still fixed upon those days, 'a certain personage' composed this verse:

The Tosa Diary

都にて山の端にみし月なれど浪より出で、浪にこそ入れ

廿一日、卯の刻ばかりに船出だす。みな人々の船出づ。これを見れば春の海に秋の木の葉しも散れるやうにぞありける。おぼろけの願によりてにやあらむ、風も吹かずよき日出できて漕ぎゆく。この間に使はれむとて、つきてくる童あり。それがうたふ船唄、

なほこそ国のかたは見やらるれ、わが父母ありとしおもへば。かへらや。

とうたふぞあはれなる。かくうたふを聞きつ、漕ぎくるに、黒鳥といふ鳥、岩のうへに集まり居り。その岩のもとに浪しろくうち寄す。楫取の言ふやう「黒鳥のもとに白

In the Capital
Oft I saw the moon arise
O'er the mountain-tops;
Now she rises from the main
Sinking in the waves again.

26 FEB. *21st day.*—The boat set forth about the Hour of the Hare (6.0 a.m.). Many other boats started as well, and the sight seemed to him like autumn leaves scattered upon the sea, although it was spring time. There was no breath of wind—no doubt in answer to their prayers for haze—and the sun was shining brightly as they set out rowing. About this time a boy who had come as his servant sang this boat song,

'Still can I cast my gaze far o'er the country-side; when I think of my father and of my mother, I long to return to them again.'[39]

It was quite pathetic to hear him singing this, and the boat rowed on while they were still listening to it. Some birds called blackbirds were clustered upon the cliffs, and at the foot of these cliffs the waves were breaking into foam. The steersman remarked, 'Under the blackbirds the white waves are breaking!' These words,

The Tosa Diary

き浪をよす」とぞ言ふ。この詞、何とにはなけれども、もの言ふやうにぞ聞こえたる。人の程にあはねば咎むるなり。かくいひつゝゆくに、船君なる人、浪を見て、国よりはじめて海賊むくいせむといふなる事を思ふへに、海のまたおそろしければ、頭もみな白けぬ。七十八十は海にあるものなりけり。

わが髪のゆきと磯べの白浪といづれまされりおきつ島もり

楫取いへ。

廿二日、よんべの泊より、こと泊を追ひてゆく。遥かに山見ゆ。年九つばかりなる男の童、年よりは幼くぞある。この童、船を漕ぐまにまに、山もゆくと見ゆるを見てあやしきこと歌をぞよめる。その歌、

whatever they might be worth, sounded remarkable, and, as he had never met a man like that before, he was much struck with them. At these words and while still traveling on, he who was 'the passenger' noticed the waves, and remembered that the pirates had threatened to take revenge upon him, when once he had left the Province; all his hair turned white, when the waves once more became rough. Seventy or eighty years are what one must expect at sea![40]

> White as snow my hair,
> Waves roll in upon the shore
> Breaking into foam;
> Which is whiter? Can'st thou say,
> Warder of the Isles, I pray?

Tell me, steersman.

27 FEB. *22nd day.*—They rowed on from last night's stopping-place to the next one. In the distance the hills were visible, and a lad on board, who was but nine years old and looked much younger, fancied that these hills seemed to be following the boat as it was being rowed along, and composed this quaint verse:

The Tosa Diary

漕ぎてゆく船にてみればあしびきの山さへゆくを松は知らずや

けふ海荒らげにて磯に雪ふり浪の花とぞいへる。幼き童のことにては、似つかはし。ある人のよめる。

浪とのみひとつに聞けど色見れば雪と花とにまがひけるかな

廿三日、日照りて曇りぬ。このわたり、海賊のおそりありといへば神仏を祈る。

廿四日、昨日の同じ所なり。

While I watch the shore
From the swiftly moving ship,
Do the pine trees guess,
That the hills on which they grow
Seem to move along also?

So he sang. How characteristic it is of a young lad's fancy! This day the sea was rough, and the waves broke into blossom, falling like snow upon the beach; whereupon 'a certain personage' composed this:

Not a sound I hear,
Save the tumult of the waves
Breaking into foam.
Much I wonder at the sight,—
Mingled snow and blossoms white!

28 FEB. *23rd day.*—The sun shone forth from the clouds, and, as there was said to be danger of pirates during the voyage, he prayed for protection to the Shintō and Buddhist Gods.

1 MAR. *24th day.*—They remained at the same place as the day before.

The Tosa Diary

廿五日、楫取らの「北風悪し」といへば、船出ださず。海賊追ひ来といふ事、絶えず聞こゆ。

廿六日、まことにやあらむ、海賊追ふといへば夜中ばかりより船を出だして漕ぎくる、途に手向けする所あり。楫取して幣たいまつらするに、幣のひむがしへ散れば楫取の申して奉ることは、「この幣の散るかたに御船速に漕がしめ給へ」と申し奉る。これを聞きてある女の童のよめる、

わたつみのちぶりの神に手向けする幣の追ひ風止まず吹かなむ

とぞよめる。この間に風のよければ楫取いたくほこりて、船に帆あげなど喜ぶ。その

2 MAR. *25th day.*—The ship's officers said the north wind was unfavourable, so the boat did not start. There were many reports going about that the pirates were actually in pursuit!

3 MAR. *26th day.*—Can this really be true? As they say the pirates are in chase, the boat is not to start before midnight, and offerings are to be made while rowing. The steersman accordingly offered prayer-papers,[41] and, as these fluttered away to the east, he prayed, 'Graciously allow our gallant ship to be rowed with all speed in the direction taken by these prayer-papers.' On hearing this a child made the following verse:

> To the Deep Sea God,
> He who rules the ocean road,
> Make we now our prayer;
> For these flying *nusa*, pray,
> May the breeze not die away.

This was her verse. As the wind was fair at the moment, the steersman was proud and happy in hoisting sail on the boat; and the women and children, as they heard the sound, were delighted, for they thought that now (they would surely arrive) sooner or later.

The Tosa Diary

音を聞きて、童も女もいつしかとし思へばにやあらむ、いたく喜ぶ。このなかに淡路の専女といふ人のよめる歌、

追風の吹きぬるときはゆく船の帆手うちてこそうれしかりけれ

とぞ。天気のことにつけて祈る。

廿七日、風吹き浪荒らければ船出ださず。これかれ、かしこく歎く。男たちの心なぐさめに、漢詩に「日を望めば都遠し」などいふなる言のさまを聞きて、ある女のよめる歌、

日をだにもあま雲ちかく見るものを都へと思ふ道のはるけさ

Among them all one called the Matron of Awaji[42] composed this:

> When the kindly breeze
> Follows up behind the boat,
> Fast we speed along;
> As we hoist the sail with glee,[43]
> Happy and content are we.

And at the same time she prayed for fine weather.

4 MAR. *27th day.*—The wind blew, the waves were rough, and the boat could not start. They were all complaining dreadfully; so the men, to cheer up their hearts, composed a Chinese poem, to the effect that the Capital was further away than the sun itself; and on hearing it a certain woman composed this:

> In the sky the clouds
> Ever nearer seem to draw,
> E'en the sun as well;
> But the Capital today
> Still seems very far away.

また、ある人のよめる、

　吹く風の絶えぬ限りし立ちくれば波路はいとゞはるけかりけり

日ひと日、風止まず。つまはじきして寝ぬ。

廿八日、夜もすがら雨止まず。けさも。

廿九日、船出だしてゆく。うらうらと照りて漕ぎゆく。爪のいと長くなりにたるを見て日を数ふれば、けふは子の日なりければ切らず。正月なれば京の子の日の事言ひ出で、、「小松もがな」といへど海中なれば難しかし。ある女の書きて出だせる歌、

To this 'a certain personage' replied:

Loud the tempests roar,
Not an instant dying down
As we travel on,
And our road across the sea
Ever longer seems to be.[44]

All day long the wind did not drop; so he snapped his fingers[45] and retired to rest.

5 MAR. *28th day.*—The rain did not stop all through the night, nor in the morning either.

6 MAR. *29th day.*—The boat set out and the sun shone brightly as they went on rowing. Noticing that his nails had grown very long, he counted the days and found that it was a 'Day of the Rat'[46]—they must not be cut. As it was the first month, they chatted about the Day of the Rat in the Capital, and wished there were some young pine trees (for them to pull up); but, as they were out at sea, such things were hard to find. A certain woman wrote this verse:

The Tosa Diary

おぼつかなけふは子の日かあまならば海松をだに引かましものを

とぞいへる。海にて子の日の歌にてはいかゞあらむ。また、ある人のよめる歌。

けふなれど若菜もつまず春日野のわが漕ぎ渡る浦になければ

かくいひつゝ、漕ぎゆく。おもしろき所に船を寄せて「こゝやいどこ」と問ひければ、「土佐の泊」といひけり。昔、土佐といひける所に住みける女、この船にまじれりけり。そが言ひけらく、「昔、しばしありし所のなくひ（名たぐひ）にぞあなる。あはれ」と言ひてよめる歌、

Is it really true
That today is *Ne no Hi*?
Were I a fish-wife,
I would dive down through the brine
And pull up the salt sea-pine.[47]

Those were her words; but how can one write a Day of the Rat verse at sea? 'A certain personage' replied with this:

Though this is the day,
Yet we cannot pick the greens
On Kasuga Moor;
Never were they known to grow
On the shore, past which we row.

They went on rowing, while he was reciting this. On the boat approaching a delightful spot, he asked what place it was, and was told it was called 'Tosa Stopping-Place'. There was a woman on board,[48] who had once lived in the land called Tosa, and she said that in past days she had known a place of that name, but only for a short time. To express her regret for it, she composed this verse:

年ごろをすみし所の名にしおへばきよる浪をもあはれとぞ見る

とぞいへる。

三十日、雨風吹かず。海賊は夜あるきせざなりと聞きて、夜中ばかりに船を出だして阿波の水門を渡る。夜中なれば、西ひむがしも見えず、男女、からく神仏を祈りて、この水門を渡りぬ。寅卯の時ばかりに、沼島といふ所を過ぎて、多奈川といふ所を渡る。からく急ぎて和泉の灘といふ所に至りぬ。けふ海に浪に似たる物なし。神仏の恵み蒙れるに似たり。けふ船に乗りし日より数ふれば、三十日あまり九日になりにけり。今は和泉の国に来ぬれば海賊ものならず。

二月朔日、あしたの間雨降る。午刻ばかりに止みぬれば、和泉の灘といふ所より出で、漕ぎゆく。海のうへ、昨日の如く風浪見えず。黒崎の松原を経てゆく。所の名は

> Musing on the name
> Of the place where once I lived
> For a year or so,—
> Billows rolling in from sea
> Come to sympathize with me.

7 MAR. *30th day.*—The wind and rain had stopped; and so, hearing that the pirates never travel by night, the boat set out to cross the Awa Channel at midnight. It was so dark that they could not see which was east and which was west; but men and women prayed earnestly to the Shintō and Buddhist Gods, and so the dreaded channel was crossed in safety. It was not till the Hour of the Tiger or the Hare (4.0 or 6.0 a.m.) that they passed the Isle of Nujima, crossed (the mouth of) the Tanagawa, and, hurrying on as fast as possible, reached the Sea of Izumi. That day there were no waves upon the sea, thanks to the blessings vouchsafed by the Shintō and Buddhist Gods. Up to date the days passed on board ship amounted to nine-and-thirty days. Now that they had reached the Land of Izumi, there was no further question of pirates.

8 MAR. *1st day of the 2nd month.*—Rain fell in the morning, and stopped only at the Hour of the Horse (noon). Passing through the Sea of Izumi, they rowed

黒く、松の色は青く、磯の浪は雪のごとくに、貝の色は蘇枋に五色にいまひと色ぞ足らぬ。この間に、けふは箱浦といふ所より綱手ひきてゆく。かくゆく間に、ある人のよめる歌、

玉くしげ箱のうら浪立たぬ日は海をかゞみとたれか見ざらむ

また船君のいはく「この月までなりぬること」と歎きて苦しきに耐へずして、人も言ふこと、て心やりにいへる、

ひく船の綱手のながき春の日をよそかいかまでわれはへにけり

on. Just as yesterday no wind-tossed waves were visible at sea. They passed the pine forest on Black Head. The name of the headland was black, the color of its pines green, the breakers upon the shore white as snow, and the tint of its shells pink; so that only one color was wanting to complete the five primary colors.[49] That day the boat was towed by a rope from the place named Casket Beach, and while traveling thus 'a certain personage' composed this:

> Not a ripple breaks
> On the shore at Casket Beach,
> Fair as jewel box;[50]
> Could the brightest looking-glass
> Such a sea as this surpass?

Once again 'the passenger' spoke, lamenting that (the voyage) had lasted into this month, and for the many hardships they had endured, to which the others agreed. Out of the fullness of his heart he recited this:

> Though the days in spring
> Grow as long as is the rope
> Used to tow our boat,
> Forty days we've spent,—maybe
> Fifty days upon the sea.

The Tosa Diary

聞く人の思へるやう、「なぞ、たゞごとなる」と、密に言ふべし。「船君のからくひねり出だしてよしと思へる事を。ゑじもこそし給べ」とて、つゝめきて止みぬ。にわかに風浪たかければとゞまりぬ。

二日、雨風止まず。日ひと日夜もすがら神仏を祈る。

三日、海の上昨日のやうなれば、船出ださず。風の吹くこと止まねば岸の浪たちかへる。これにつけてよめる歌、

　緒をよりてかひなきものはおちつもる涙の玉をぬかぬなりけり

かくて、けふ暮れぬ。

People who hear this will say to themselves that this kind of stuff is very poor. But 'the passenger' produced it with a good deal of difficulty and thought it pretty good; so they should stop whispering such cruel things about it. But suddenly the wind and waves got up, and so they had to stop talking.

9 MAR. *2nd day.*—The wind and rain did not cease. For a whole day and night they prayed to the Shintō and Buddhist Gods.

10 MAR. *3rd day.*—Out at sea it was just like yesterday, so the boat did not start. The howling gale did not abate, and the waves dashed up against the cliffs and drew back again. Noting this, he composed the following:

Fast my teardrops fall,
But to twist a silken thread
Surely would be vain;
Who could thread up pearls so frail?
All my skill would not avail.[51]

And thus the day drew to its close.

四日、楫取「けふ風雲の気色はなはだ悪し」といひて、船出だきずなりぬ。然れども、ひねもすに浪風立たず。この楫取は日もえ計らぬかたるなりけり。この泊の浜には、種々の麗しき貝、石など多かり。かゝればたゞ昔の人をのみ恋ひつゝ、船なる人のよめる、

　　よする浪うちも寄せなむわが恋ふる人わすれ貝おりてひろはむ

といへれば、ある人の耐へずして船の心やりによめる、

　　わすれ貝ひろひしもせじ白玉を恋ふるをだにもかたみと思はむ

11 MAR. *4th day.*—The steersman said that the wind-blown clouds looked very threatening today, so the boat did not set out. However, the wind and waves did not get up the whole day long; this steersman was not always right in his forecasts of the weather. Beautiful shells of many kinds and pebbles were plentiful on the shore where they camped; and with reference to them somebody belonging to the ship composed this verse in memory of one who was much loved:

> Here the breaking waves
> Come and go, as I lament
> For my darling child;
> Stooping I, to bid farewell,
> Pick up a 'forgetting-shell'.[52]

Such were her words; but 'a certain personage', unable to bear it any longer, composed this, to give heart to the others in the ship:

> Here no more we'll stray
> Seeking for 'forgetting-shells';
> But a dainty pearl
> Pure and white might serve to tell
> Of the child we loved so well.

となむいへる。女児のためには親をさなくなりぬべし。「珠ならずもありけむを」と人いはむや。されども、「死にし子顔よかりき」と、いふやうもあり。なほ同じ所に日を経ることを歎きて、ある女のよめる歌、

手をひで、寒さも知らぬ泉にぞ汲むとはなしに日ごろ経にける

五日、けふ、からくして和泉の灘より小津の泊を追ふ。松原、目もはるばるなり。これかれ苦しければよめる歌、

ゆけどなほゆきやられぬは妹がうむ小津の浦なる岸の松原

Thus he spoke in memory of his little daughter, for a parent is apt to become very childish. Some may object that she was not like a pearl; be that as it may, the child is dead, and it is no empty compliment to say she had a beautiful face. A certain woman composed this verse in grief at the number of days spent in the same place:

> Long we've soaked our hands
> In Izumi's icy spring
> Dreading not the cold;
> Here though many days we waste,
> 'Tis a spring we never taste.[53]

12 MAR. *5th day.*—This day with difficulty they hastened on through the Sea of Izumi to the Stopping-Place of Ozu. To his eye the pine forests seemed never-ending, everything seemed to have gone wrong, and he composed this:

> Though we speed along,
> Yet the pine trees on the cliffs
> Never seem to pass;
> Long as thread is Ozu strand
> Spun out by a maiden's hand.[54]

かくいひつゝ、来る程に「船疾く漕げ。日のよきに」と催せば、楫取、船子どもにいはく「御船より仰せたぶなり。朝北の出で来ぬさきに、綱手はや引け」と言ふ。この詞の歌のやうなるは、楫取のおのづからの詞なり。楫取はうつたへに、われ歌のやうなる事言ふとにもあらず。聞く人の「あやしく歌めきても言ひつるかな」とて、書き出だせれば、げに三十文字あまりなりけり。けふ「浪な立ちそ」と、人々ひねもすに祈るしるしありて、風浪立たず。今し、鴎むれ居てあそぶ所あり。京のちかづくよろびのあまりに、ある童のよめる歌、

いのりくる風間と思ふをあやなくに鴎さへだに浪と見ゆらむ

といひてゆく間に、石津といふ所の松原おもしろくて、浜辺遠し。また住吉のわたりを漕ぎゆく。ある人のよめる歌、

At these words and while they still traveled on, the steersman called to the sailors to pull hard, for the weather was about to improve. 'On this gallant ship my command must be obeyed; this is what I say,—ere the morning north wind blow, get the rope ashore and tow,' said he. The poetic form of these words was quite unintentional on the part of the steersman; and, on being appealed to, he said he did not mean it for a verse; but, on putting into writing the queer poetical sentence the man was heard to say, there proved indeed to be just over thirty syllables (i.e. thirty-one syllables).[55] This day every one prayed all day long that the waves outside might not arise; and in answer to their prayers the wind and waves did not get up. Soon (they arrived at) a place where flocks of seagulls sported about, and, in an excess of joy at getting so near the Capital, a child composed this:

> Though the wind has dropped,
> For the Gods have heard our prayers,
> In my dizzy brain
> Swooping seagulls look to me
> Like the ever surging sea.

While she recited this, they traveled on. The pine forest at a place called Iwatsu was very beautiful, but the shore seemed interminable. Once more, as they rowed

The Tosa Diary

いま見てぞ身をば知りぬる住江の松よりさきにわれは経にけり

こゝにむかしへ人の母、ひと日片時もわすれねばよめる、

住江に船さしよせよわすれ草しるしありやとつみてゆくべく

となむ。うったへに忘れなむとにはあらで、恋しき心地しばしやすめて、またも恋ふる力にせむとなるべし。かく言ひて眺めつゝ、来る間に、ゆくりなく風吹きて漕げども、後方しぞきにしぞきて、ほとほとしくうちはめつべし。楫取のいはく「この住吉の明神は、例の神ぞかし。ほしき物ぞおはすらむ」とは、今めくものか。さて「幣を奉り給へ」と言ふ。言ふにしたがひて幣たいまつる。かくたいまつれれども、も

past Sumiyoshi, 'a certain personage' composed this:

> Suminoye's pines,[56]
> As I watch them, seem to be
> Younger far than I;
> I shall vanish from the scene,
> But the pines are evergreen.

And here the mother of one now gone, whom she never forgets for a day, or even for a moment:

> Urge the boat along,
> On to Suminoye beach,
> For I long to pick
> Some 'forgetting-grass',[57] to see
> If it will come true with me.

This she said, not because she wished to forget really, but she hoped that her sorrow might find some short relief, in order that her love might return stronger than ever. With these words then they traveled on, while still gazing at the prospect. But suddenly the wind arose; and, though they rowed hard, they drifted quickly astern and nearly capsized, when they must all have been lost. The steersman said, 'This holy Deity of Sumiyoshi is a well-known God, and he desires some gift.' How like every-

The Tosa Diary

はら風止まで、いや吹きに、いや立ちに、風浪の危ふければ楫取またいはく「幣には御心のいかねば、御船もゆかぬなり。なほうれしと思ひ給ふべき物たいまつり給べ」と言ふ。また言ふに従ひて「いかゞはせむ」とて「眼もこそ二つあれ。ただひとつある鏡をたいまつる」とて、海にうちはめつれば口惜し。されば、うちつけに海は鏡の面のごととなりぬれば、ある人のよめる歌、

ちはやぶる神の心をあるゝ海に鏡を入れてかつ見つるかな

いたく住江の忘れ草、岸の姫松などいふ神にはあらずかし。目もうつらうつら鏡に神の心をこそは見つれ。楫取の心は神の御心なりけり。

body else! Someone suggested that *nusa* should be offered; so accordingly an offering of prayer-papers was made. But, though it was done chiefly for the wind to abate, it began to blow harder than ever and the waves rose accordingly, so that they were in great danger. Then the steersman spoke again, and said, 'As the august heart (of the God) has not been moved by the prayer-papers, the gallant ship cannot proceed; in making an offering, therefore, something should be presented that will be thought of value.' Accordingly, what was to be done! He had two eyes, but could offer only one mirror[58]; so to his deep regret it was thrown into the sea. Well, immediately the sea became as calm as the looking-glass itself! and 'a certain personage' composed this:

> In the raging sea
> I have cast my looking-glass,
> And the gift's result
> Shows the partiality
> Of the awful Deity.

Verily there are no Gods as kindly as the 'forgetting-grass' of Suminoye or the delicate pines upon its cliffs. Plainly in the mirror could his eyes see the august heart of the God—which was remarkably like the heart of the steersman![59]

六日、澪標のもとより出で、難波につきて河尻に入る。みな人々、媼、翁、額に手をあて、喜ぶこと二つなし。かの船酔の淡路の島の大御、都近くなりぬといふを喜びて、船底より頭をもたげてかくぞ言へる、

　いつしかといぶせかりつる難波がた蘆こぎそけて御船来にけり

いと思ひの外なる人の言へれば、人々あやしがる。これが中に、心地なやむ船君、いたく愛で、「船酔したうべりし御顔には似ずもあるかな」といひける。

七日、けふは河尻に船入り立ちて漕ぎ上るに、川の水乾て悩みわずらふ。船の上ることいと難し。かかる間に船君の病者もとよりこちごちしき人にて、かうやうの事、

13 MAR. *6th day.*—They left Miotsukushi,[60] reached the port of Naniwa and entered the mouth of the river. Everyone, men, women, and children, lifted their hands to their foreheads and exclaimed in delight, 'There is nothing like this!' The Old Lady of Awaji Isle was sea-sick; but on hearing that they were getting near the Capital, she raised her head from the bottom of the boat and in her delight recited this verse:

> Many doubts had I
> On the day we first set forth;
> Now our gallant ship
> Gently glides, from danger far,
> 'Mid the reeds of Naniwa.

Everybody was astonished when she came out with this so unexpectedly; and among them 'the passenger', who was also feeling unwell, praised it very highly, and said it was not what he had expected from one with such a sea-sick countenance.

14 MAR. *7th day.*—This day the boat left the mouth of the river; but as they rowed on, the river tide was ebbing, and they were in great difficulty. To get the boat up was very hard. At this 'the sick passenger', who

更に知らざりけり。かれども淡路専女の歌に愛でゝ、都誇りにもやあらむ、からくしてあやしき歌ひねり出だせり。その歌は、

　来と来ては川上り路の水をあさみ船も我が身もなづむけふかな

これは病をすればよめるなるべし。

　とくと思ふ船なやますは我がために水のこゝろのあさきなりけり

この歌は、都近くなりぬるよろこびに耐へずして、言へるなるべし。淡路御の歌におとれり。「ねたき。言はざらましものを」とくやしがるうちに、夜になりて寝にけり。

was not very practical by nature, was wholly at a loss to know what should be done. However, he was so pleased with the Matron of Awaji's verse, that he comforted himself with the thought that he would soon be at the Capital; and so with some difficulty he turned out this very doubtful verse:

> Here at last are we,
> But how shallow runs the stream
> In the river bed;
> Further can the boat not go,
> Here must we remain also.

It was because he was so unwell that he composed this poor sort of thing. As he was not satisfied with it, here is another:

> Fast we'd hurry on,
> If the river's shallow bed
> Did not stay our boat.
> As the stream runs dry, maybe
> It has got a grudge at me.

These verses should be understood as composed when he could not repress his joy at getting so near the Capital; but they are not as good as the one by her

八日、なほ川上りになづみて、鳥養御牧といふほとりに泊る。こよひ船君例の病起りていたく悩む。ある人、あざらかなる物持てきたり。米して返り事す。男ども密にいふなり「飯ぼして持つゝる」とや。かうやうの事、所々にあり。けふ、節忌すれば、魚不用。

九日、心もとなさに明けぬから、船をひきつゝ上れども、川の水なければるざりにのみぞゐざる。この間に、和田の泊のあかれの所といふ所あり。米、魚など乞へば、おこなひつ。かくて船ひき上るに渚院といふ所を見つゝゆく。その院、昔を思ひやりて見れば、おもしろかりける所なり。後方なる岡には松の木どもあり。中の庭には梅

Ladyship of Awaji, and feeling jealous of her he regretted having made them; so, as the night was drawing on, he retired to sleep.

15 MAR. *8th day.*—Still keeping to the river-side, they stopped at a place called 'The Gamekeeper's Preserve'. That evening 'the passenger' suffered severely from his chronic complaint.[61] There was a man who came with some trifling gift, who got some rice in return (i.e. a large present); and the men whispered among themselves, that he had come 'to fish with a grain of rice'. But this sort of thing may happen anywhere. This day he was fasting and ate no fish.

16 MAR. *9th day.*—From early dawn he was very anxious. They ascended the river towing the boat; but, as there was hardly any water in the river, they had to push and haul it along. At last they came to a place called 'The Parting of the Ways' at the Stopping-Place of Wada, and there rice and fish were supplied to them at their request. While towing the boat up like this, they saw on their way a place called 'The Shore Residence'. This Residence, as one pictured to oneself the days of old, was a very delightful spot. On the hill behind were

The Tosa Diary

の花さけり。ここに人々のいはく「これ、むかし名高く聞えたる所なり。故惟喬親王のおほむ供に、故在原業平中将の、

世の中に絶えて桜のさかざらば春の心はのどけからまし

といふ歌よめる所なりけり。」いま興ある人、所に似たる歌よめり、

千代へたる松にはあれどいにしへの声の寒さはかはらざりけり

またある人のよめる、

many pine trees, while in the garden in front the plum trees were in full blossom. Here, they said, here was a place famous in past days; for on this spot General Ariwara no Narihira lived in companionship with His Royal Highness Prince Koretaka.

> If the cherry trees
> Nevermore burst forth in bloom,
> 'Twould be better far;
> For the saddest time of all
> Is the spring, when petals fall.'[62]

And this is the spot where he composed this verse. Now 'a certain personage' in his delight at the place composed this:

> For a thousand years
> Have these pine trees lived, their tops
> Rustle as of old;
> 'Tis a language drear and strange,
> And their voice will never change.

This, also, he composed:

The Tosa Diary

君恋ひて世をふる宿の梅の花昔の香にぞなほにほひける

といひつゝぞ、都の近づくを喜びつゝ上る。かく上る人々の内に京よりくだりし時に、みな人、子どもなかりき、いたれりし国にてぞ、子生める者どもありあへる。人みな船の泊まる所に、子を抱きつゝ、おりのりす。これを見て、昔の子の母悲しきに耐へずして、

なかりしもありつ、帰る人の子をありしもなくてくるが悲しさ

といひてぞ泣きける。父もこれを聞きて、いかゞあらむ。かうやうの事も歌も、好むとてあるにもあらざるべし。唐もこゝも、思ふことに耐へぬ時のわざとか。こよひ、鵜殿といふ所に泊る。

> Still the plum trees bloom
> Round this dwelling as of old,
> And in memory
> Of their Lord they loved so well
> Still retain their ancient smell.[63]

While these were being recited, they went on rejoicing at getting nearer to the Capital. Among all the people thus going up, not one had any children when they left the Capital; but some had babies born in the Province. Everybody crowded down to the place where the boat stopped to embrace these children, and at the sight of this the mother of that child who is gone could no longer restrain her grief:

> Many who set forth
> Childless from the Capital
> Bring a baby back;
> One who then a daughter had
> Now returns bereft and sad.

With these words she wept. And when 'the father' heard it, what could he do? He wished to make a similar verse, but there was no other subject. For here, as in China, (we compose a poem) when our hearts are too full of feeling. That evening they stopped at a place called Udono.

十日、さはる事ありて上らず。

十一日、雨いささか降りて止みぬ。かくてさし上るに、ひむがしの方に、山の横ほれるを見て人に問へば「八幡宮」と言ふ。これを聞きて喜びて人々拝み奉る。山崎の橋見ゆ。嬉しきこと限りなし。こゝに相應寺のほとりに、しばし船をとゞめて、とかく定むる事あり。この寺の岸のほとりに柳多くあり。ある人、この柳のかげの川の底にうつれるを見てよめる歌、

　さざれ浪寄するあやをば青柳のかげのいとして織るかとぞ見る

十二日、山崎に泊れり。

17 MAR. *10th day.*—There was something wrong and they did not go forward.

18 MAR. *11th day.*—Gentle rain was falling, so they remained where they were for a little. Then, on going forward, (something) came into view to the east across the mountains, which a man on being asked said was the Temple of Hachiman.[64] On hearing this they all reverently made obeisance and offered prayers. See! there is Yamasaki Bridge! There was no limit to their delight; and there, opposite the Sōō Temple, the boat stopped for a little time, while they made their various arrangements. Near the precincts of this temple were many willow trees, and 'a certain personage' seeing them reflected at the bottom of the river composed this:

> Looking o'er the stream,
> Imaged on the rippling waves
> As they come and go,
> Hanging willow branches green
> Woven like silk threads are seen.

19 MAR. *12th day.*—They remained at Yamasaki.

The Tosa Diary

十三日、なほ山崎に。

十四日、雨ふる。けふ車、京へとりにやる。

十五日、けふ車ゐてきたり。船のむつかしさに船より人の家にうつる。このあるじの、またあるじのよきを見るに、うたて思ほゆ。いろいろに返り事す。家の人の出で入り、にくげならず、ゐや、かなり。

十六日、けふの夜さりつかた京へ上るついでに見れば山崎の小櫃の絵も、まがりのおほぢの形も変らざりけり。「売人の心をぞしらぬ」とぞ言ふなる。かくて京へいくに、

The Tosa Diary

20 MAR. *13th day.*—Still at Yamasaki.

21 MAR. *14th day.*—Rain fell. This day he sent to the Capital for a carriage.[65]

22 MAR. *15th day.*—This day the carriage arrived. Owing to the dirt on board he removed from the boat to the house of a friend. This friend's house seemed indeed a delightful change, and its owner treated him with the greatest kindness; so much so that he felt quite sorry for troubling him, and tried to make returns in many ways. Those who entered and left the house, too, were by no means disagreeable people, but cultivated gentlefolk.

23 MAR. *16th day.*—That evening, as he went up to the Capital, he saw in the shops at Yamasaki the little boxes painted with pictures and the rice-cakes twisted into the shape of conch shells, just the same as ever; and he wondered if the hearts of the shopkeepers also were the same.[66] After this, on the road to the Capital, many people, and not necessarily his own relations, entertained him at Shimasaka. Indeed, they were more hos-

The Tosa Diary

島坂にて、人あるじしたり。必ずしもあるまじきわざなり。立ちてゆきし時よりは来る時ぞ人はとかくありける。これにも返り事す。夜になして京には入らむと思へば、急ぎしもせぬ程に月出でぬ。桂川、月あかきにぞ渡る。人々のいはく「この川飛鳥川にあらねば、淵瀬更に変らざりけり」といひてある人のよめる歌、

　　ひさかたの月におひたる桂川そこなる影も変らざりけり

またある人のいへる、

　　あまぐものはるかなりつる桂川袖をひで、も渡りぬるかな

また、ある人よめり。

pitable on his return than when he set out, and in some way or other he would have liked to make some return for it. Planning to arrive at the Capital by night, he did not hasten. The moon had risen, and he crossed the Katsura River in bright moonlight. Every one said that as this was not the Asuka River,[67] it would not suddenly change itself to eddies and rapids; and 'a certain personage' composed this:

> 'Neath the moon of heaven
> Flows the River Katsura
> Slowly growing old;
> In its depths the moon lies low
> As it did long, long ago.[68]

He recited this also:

> Once Katsura's Stream
> Seemed to me as far away
> As the clouds of heaven;
> Now, while crossing, I perceive
> It has wet my dipping sleeve.

And again he composed this:

桂川わが心にもかよはねど同じふかさにながるべらなり

京の嬉しきあまりに、歌もあまりぞ多かる。夜更けてくれば所々も見えず。京に入り立ちてうれし。家にいたりて門に入るに、月明かければ、いとよく有様見ゆ。聞きしよりもまして、いふかひなくぞこぼれ破れたる。家に預けたりつる人の心も荒れたるなりけり。中垣こそあれ、ひとつ家のやうなれば、のぞみて預かれるなり。さるは、便りごとに物も絶えず得させたり。今宵「かゝること」と、声高にものも言はせず。いとはつらく見ゆれど、志をばせむとす。さて池めいてくぼまり、水ける所あり。ほとりに松もありき。五年六年のうちに千年や過ぎにけむ、かたへはなくなりにけり。いま生ひたるぞまじれる。大方の皆荒にたれば、「あはれ」とぞ人々言ふ。思ひ出でぬ事なく思ひ恋ひしきがうちに、この家にて生れし女児のもろともに帰らねばいかゞは

> Well I know my heart
> And the River Katsura
> Never were alike;
> Yet in depth my heart would seem
> Not unlike the flowing stream.

These too many verses are due to his excessive pleasure at reaching the Capital. The night was growing late and some places could not be seen, but it was delightful to enter the Capital once more. On reaching his home and entering his door, the moon was so bright that he could see the state of things at a glance. Needless to say the whole place was hopelessly overgrown and ragged, even more than he had been told! The heart of the man, to whom he had entrusted his home, must be as waste as it! Their two houses, separated only by a hedge, looked as if they were both one, so he had hopefully left it in his charge, and had never failed to send him a present on every opportunity. Well, that evening he determined he would not speak about it in a loud tone of voice; and, though he felt very angry, he had to make some sort of acknowledgement. Then, again, the ground had sunk and was full of water, as if it was a pond. There was a pine tree close by, and it had overgrown in five or six years, as if in a thousand years; half its branches were dead, and the young growing ones all in confusion. Almost everything

悲しき。船人も皆、子たかりてのゝしる。かゝるうちに、なほ悲しきに耐へずして密に心知れる人といへりける歌、

生まれしも帰らぬものを我がやどに小松のあるを見るが悲しさ

とぞいへる。なほあかずやあらむ、またかくなむ。

見し人の松の千年に見ましかば遠く悲しき別れせましや

わすれがたく、口惜しきこと多かれど、え尽くさず。とまれかうまれ、疾くやりてむ。

was the same, and everybody offered him their sympathy. He recalled especially how his little daughter had been born in that house, in its beloved interior; how sad it was that she had not returned with them! The sailors and others were talking loudly as they embraced their children, and just then his grief was more that he could bear; so to one who sympathized with his feelings he softly whispered this verse:

> Never to return.
> To our home where she was born;
> Ah, how pitiful!
> Yet the pine tree shoots live on,
> Though our little girl is gone.

Thus he spoke. And if that is not enough, here is yet one more:

> Could I have endowed
> With the pine tree's thousand years
> One I used to see,
> Parted from her nevermore
> All my sorrows would be o'er.

His sorrows, which he can never forget, are more than he can ever express. Well, well,—this must be torn up at once.

NOTES

1

As explained in the Introduction, this opening sentence means that the diary is to be written in 'the women's language', i.e. in phonetic characters only, without the use of ideographs; and, in order to be consistent, Tsurayuki writes as if he was a woman, and mentions himself only in the third person, using different names, such as 'a certain personage', 'the seafarer', &c.

2

29 JAN. *Uma no hanamuke* means to 'turn your horse's nose', which was an old expression corresponding to our 'stirrup cup'; it gradually came to mean any kind of farewell present made to one about to start on a journey. In this case it evidently took the form of *saké*, and Tsurayuki himself notices how incongruous the expression is for one about to travel by sea. Elsewhere I have translated it simply 'to make a farewell present'.

3

29 JAN. Salt is generally used to preserve food, and one would therefore naturally expect it to preserve the travelers; but here we find them, by the side of a whole ocean of salt water, *azare*, literally 'gōne bad'—like tainted meat or fish.

4
31 JAN. This refers to the staggering footprints of the intoxicated sailors on the shore. They were illiterate men, unable to form a single ideographic character; but Tsurayuki noticed that their feet had unconsciously made the character for 'ten', which is similar to our sign for plus. An alternative reading is that they staggered in ten different directions; for *tomoji*, if written in phonetics only as the original was, would give both meanings. There seems to be another play upon words here also; for *ashi wa, to-*, if read as one word *ashiato*, means 'footprints'.

5
1 FEB. This is the official residence of the Governor of Tosa, recently occupied by Tsurayuki, but now given up to his successor, the new Governor.

6
2 FEB. The Chinese poems are not given, because the writer, in his assumed rôle of a woman, would not be supposed to understand them or be able to write them down. This same expression *Kara uta*, or Chinese poem, is frequently used elsewhere in the diary, meaning noth-

ing more than 'classical verse', i.e. the *tanka*, of which so many examples are given.

7
3 FEB. This was a little girl, nine years of age, who had been born in Kyōto, the Capital, and who accompanied her father to Tosa on his appointment to the Governorship. She had recently died, and her parents were inconsolable for her loss.

8
3 FEB. That is, a brother of the newly appointed Governor.

9
3 FEB. *Oshi* means 'regret', as I have translated it, but it also suggests *oshi-dori* (mandarin ducks), which, as a symbol of happy married life, might refer to Tsurayuki and his wife; while *ashi kamo* (the ducks among the reeds) are the friends who have come to bid farewell.

10
3 FEB. This steersman, who acts as captain of the ship, is a character of great interest to Tsurayuki, who continually mentions him in the course of his diary.

11

3 FEB. *Kai-uta* can mean either 'a song of the East' or 'a song of the sea', and probably both meanings are intended here. The Province of Kōshū, which lies to the east of the Capital, Kyōto, is also called *Kai*. *Sai-Koku*, the land of the West, refers to the Province of Tosa, because it lies west of Kyōto. The dust blowing about in the cabin and the clouds scudding across the sky are supposed to be agitated by the beauty of the songs they have just heard sung.

12

3 FEB. These two faithful friends, Fujiwara no Tokisané and Tachibana no Suehira, follow the departing Governor to Ōminato, the last spot in Tosa Province at which the boat stops, and bid him a final farewell ten days later.

13

5 FEB. The doctor's present was to enable the travelers to celebrate the New Year with all due honors. Spiced *saké* was then drunk to ensure long life. *Byakusan* (lit. 'white powder') was, according to the dictionaries, a composition of Japanese pepper, cassia, campanula, and *atractylis ovata*, of which some parts, probably the roots or seeds, were dried, ground up small, mixed together, and added to the *saké*.

6 FEB. These references are all to the customs and ceremonies of the New Year. Potatoes were eaten then, to imply a wish that your family might be as numerous as the potatoes on one plant. Seaweed was a symbol of good luck, and is supposed to refer to the recorded fact that when the Empress Jingō was about to embark with her armies for the subjugation of Korea in the year A.D. 202, her horses ran short of fodder; so she caused them to be fed on seaweed, which so refreshed and invigorated them that she secured a complete victory. Rice-cakes, made in the form of a mirror, were supposed to harden the teeth if eaten at the New Year, and mullet heads were sucked, it is said, to express a wish that you might be the head of a family. Tsurayuki had no mullets (*nayoshi*), but he had one trout (*oshiayu*), the names of which are not very dissimilar in the original; so the ship's company did the best they could by sucking it in turn, a process which evidently struck the writer as very disgusting. His thoughts turned longingly to Kyōto, where the New Year was being celebrated in a proper manner. The straw rope with tufts of straw or cut paper at intervals was hung over the doors of houses at the New Year; it commemorated the straw rope hung across the mouth of the cave in the time of the Gods, which prevented the Sun Goddess from retiring again, after she had been enticed out.

15

12 FEB. *Ao Uma* is literally a blue (or green) horse, i.e. a grey horse. On the seventh day of the first month ten sacred grey horses, which were kept at a temple in Kyōto, were solemnly paraded before the Emperor, while priestesses performed a sacred dance. Tsurayuki regrets that he can only see white waves now, when he would much rather be watching the parade of the grey horses.

16

12 FEB. *Iké* means a pond or pool, and one would naturally expect carp to come from an estate bearing that name; but the writer says the present consisted of nearly every other kind of fish, but not carp.

17

12 FEB. *Wakana*, green vegetables or young green shoots, were always picked on the seventh day of the first month.

18

12 FEB. *Warawa* means a child, and there is nothing in the text to say whether it was a boy or a girl. But the Kōgi edition, which I have used, adds in a note that it was probably the latter, because in the *Gosenshū* (a collection of poetry) there is a verse attributed to a daughter of Tsurayuki, who might therefore be this child.

19

13 FEB. The original verse by Ariwara no Narihira, who lived A.D. 825-80, is found in the Seventeenth Book of the *Kokinshū*, and runs:

> Akanaku ni
> Madaki mo tsuki no
> Kakururu ka
> Yama no ha nigete
> Irezu mo aranan.

> Now the lovely moon,
> Though I fain would watch it still,
> Hides away from sight.
> Would the hills but fly away
> Longer might the moonlight stay.

20

13 FEB. The River of the Sky is the Japanese name for the Milky Way; the moon is supposed to be floating on it like a boat. Ōminato, where they have been detained ever since the twenty-eighth day of the previous month, means 'the great harbor', and Tsurayuki no doubt refers to this in the verse (*izuru minato* = leaving port).

21

14 FEB. A pine tree is reputed to live for a thousand years, and both it and the stork are emblems of long life.

22

14 FEB. This very irregular composition seems to be a kind of folk-song. *Shūtome* in the seventh line is really a 'mother-in-law', and not 'mother', as I have given it.

23

14 FEB. These are Tsurayuki and his wife, who are suffering from sea-sickness, which attacked all the passengers this day, and which was no doubt the reason of their not traveling on the following day.

24

16 FEB. *Hané* means the wing or feathers of a bird.

25

16 FEB. The whole verse is to be found in the Ninth Book of the *Kokinshū*, where it is stated to be by an unknown writer. A husband and wife journeyed together to a distant part of the country, where the husband died, and the sorrowing wife retraced her steps alone to the Capital. On the journey a flock of wild geese passed her with mournful cries as they flew north again after wintering in warm climates, and she then composed this verse. It runs:

> Kita e yuku
> Kari zo nakunaru
> Tsurete koshi
> Kazu wa tarade zo
> Kaeru-bera naru.

> Wild geese heading north
> With a sad and mournful cry,
> Whom do you lament?
> Was there in the flock last year
> One who does not reappear?

26
16 FEB. Note the three long lines in the original all beginning with *omoi* (thought, care, anxiety), which I have tried in vain to reproduce in the translation.

27
18 FEB. They evidently took advantage of some one of the natural hot-springs in the neighbourhood, of which there are so many in Japan.

28

18 FEB. The God of the Sea, jealous of such a blaze of wealth and beauty, might have brought destruction upon the ship. The words within brackets are unsuited for translation.

29

20 FEB. Rice and bean gruel used to be eaten on the first, fifteenth, and twenty-eighth days of the month, which is probably the reason why the writer mentions its omission on this occasion. As it was an inauspicious day for traveling, they might have courted disaster if they had moved at their usual rate.

30

21 FEB. This is hardly correct. It was twenty-five days since he left his official residence, but he spent six days in feasting before he really started.

31

22 FEB. The Japanese say that they see a *katsura* bush growing on the face of the moon.

32

22 FEB. Possibly both these verses are by Tsurayuki, for both are attributed to *aru hito* (a certain personage); but the Kōgi edition, which I have used, offers no opinion about it.

33
22 FEB. The word I have translated 'ship's officers' is the plural of *kajitori*, a steersman, which is generally used here for the captain of the ship. The plural form occurs again on the second of March.

34
23 FEB. 'The venerable master of the ship' is no doubt intended for Tsurayuki himself, although the Kōgi edition suggests as an alternative that it means the steersman. His gloomy thoughts perhaps refer to the death of his little daughter, to which he constantly makes allusion. In the following verse he combines both the similes expressed in his former attempts.

35
23 FEB. As explained in the Introduction, the *tanka* or short verse was limited to thirty-one syllables.

36
25 FEB. Abe no Naka Maro was one of the greatest of the old poets, he died in the year A.D. 780. He had been sent on a mission to China, some say to discover the

secret of the Chinese calendar, and he composed the verse which follows at a farewell banquet in the year A.D. 726, just before he started on his way home to Japan.

37

25 FEB. This well-known verse is included in the anthology called *Hyaku Nin Isshū*; but there the first line is given as *Ama no hara*, which would change the translation to 'I, while gazing up, far into the heav'nly sky'. The Temple of Kasuga was near Nara, Naka Maro's home, and the verse expresses his feelings of home-sickness.

38

25 FEB. The Chinese, of course, would not understand the Japanese spoken language when they heard the verse recited, but when written in their own ideographic characters it would be perfectly plain to them.

39

26 FEB. This is the boat song as given, but there are two syllables too many for a *tanka* verse, and it is hard to discover any metre in it.

40

26 FEB. Tsurayuki as Governor had had to dispense

justice to these pirates, and they had threatened to take their revenge if they caught him at sea. He is afraid that they may now take him at a disadvantage if they meet him, for the sea is getting rough. His hair almost turns white with fear; but, as he says, dangers are so common at sea that it is only what one must expect.

41
3 MAR. These *nusa*, or *gohei* as they are generally called now, are pieces of white paper cut in a particular shape. Originally they represented votive offerings of pure white silk or cloth, and they are generally to be seen at Shintō Temples.

42
3 MAR. This is one of Tsurayuki's attendants, possibly his housekeeper, who was, no doubt, a native of Awaji Island.

43
3 MAR. *Hote uchite* is supposed to mean 'hoisting sail', taking *hote* as a contraction for *ho no te* or *hozuna*, 'a halyard'.

44
4 MAR. A possible second meaning of this verse would be:

Loud the tempests roar,
Not an instant dying down,
And the waves arise.
Up and down the billows will
Make our journey longer still.

This would necessitate reading *nami-ji* as two words (when the waves arise our road becomes longer and longer).

45

4 MAR. To snap the fingers was to ward off bad luck, in this case in the hope of making the wind die down.

46

6 MAR. Instead of our week the Japanese used to use the Chinese twelve-day period, each day being called after one of the Signs of the Zodiac, of which the Rat was the first. The first Rat Day of the year, or *Ne no Hi*, was always kept as a holiday, when the proper thing to do was to go out and pick the fresh green sprouts of early spring, and pull up young pine-tree shoots to ensure a long life.

47

6 MAR. *Umi-matsu*, literally 'sea-pine', is a name for

coral. The idea is that a fisherwoman, being on the sea for the Day of the Rat, would do the best she could to pluck up a young pine by diving for coral (sea-pine).

48

6 MAR. Possibly this woman may be intended for Tsurayuki himself, the former Governor of Tosa, in his character of a female writer. Or it may be his wife or one of his suite to whom he refers.

49

8 MAR. The five primary colors, according to the Japanese, are black, white, red, blue (or green), and yellow.

50

8 MAR. *Tamakushige* is a conventional poetical epithet, meaning 'like a box of pearls', here very aptly used, for Hako no Ura, the place they were passing, means 'Casket Beach'.

51

10 MAR. *Tama* means a pearl or jewel, or when used with *namida* (tears) it means teardrops. This verse is a play upon the double meaning; if only his teardrops were real pearls, he would preserve them by stringing them on a thread.

52

11 MAR. *Wasure-gai*, literally 'forgetting-shell', is a black and grey clam shell, often mentioned in old Japanese poetry. Its signification is the exact opposite of our forget-me-not flower. The writer of this verse is supposed to have been Tsurayuki's wife, the mother of his dead child.

53

11 MAR. This is a play upon the word Izumi, the name of the Province on whose shores they were camping, which means 'a spring of water'. I have had to use the word twice to bring out the meaning in the translation.

54

12 MAR. *Imo ga umu* is a conventional poetical epithet meaning 'like a maiden spinning'. It is used here with Ozu, because *o* is the word for 'thread'. But, as a matter of fact, *o* in this case means 'little', for Ozu is 'the little harbor'.

55

12 MAR. See Introduction for a note on the *tanka* metre. The *ō* in *ōse-tabu* counts as two syllables.

56

12 MAR. Suminoye and Sumiyoshi are one and the same place.

57

12 MAR. *Wasure-gusa* (forgetting-grass) is an old word for reeds or rushes, which seem to have grown in great profusion about Naniwa and Suminoye. The name is used in the same sense as the forgetting-shells mentioned in the entry for the previous day.

58

12 MAR. The old Japanese mirror was made of bronze with a highly polished face, and a back generally elaborately decorated.

59

12 MAR. This sly cut at the steersman shows that Tsurayuki, who was genuinely distressed at the loss of his mirror, was sceptical about the God of Suminoye.

60

13 MAR. *Miotsukushi* means 'a tide gauge'. It was set up off the port of Naniwa, and is frequently mentioned in old Japanese poetry.

61

15 MAR. A note in the Kōgi edition says that this chronic complaint was some disease of old age; otherwise one would have thought it might have had reference to the remains of his attack of sea-sickness, from which he had not yet recovered. 'To fish with a grain of rice' is equivalent to our expression 'to fish with a sprat for a whale'.

62

16 MAR. This verse by Ariwara no Narihira is to be found in the First Book of the *Kokinshū*.

63

16 MAR. *Furu*, in the second line, has a double meaning. If taken with *yado*, it means 'an old (house)'; but if taken with *yo wo*, it means '(the blossoms) spend (their lives, &c.)'.

64

18 MAR. Hachiman is the God of War.

65

21 MAR. *Kuruma* here does not mean a jinrikisha, which is a modern innovation of the nineteenth century.

66
23 MAR. Does this hint that Tsurayuki had on a former occasion found the shopkeepers not quite honest?

67
23 MAR. The Asuka River, notorious for sudden spates and rapids, was as uncertain as its name, which, read as *asu ka*, means 'Who knows what the morrow will bring?'

68
23 MAR. A second meaning is that the *katsura* bush, which is supposed to be visible on the face of the moon, is growing old, but still the moon's reflection in the Katsura River remains the same.